How to Shoe a Horse

How to Shoe a Horse

Marion C. Manwill

Photographs by Kine Hatch
Illustrations by Marion C. Manwill

South Brunswick and New York: A. S. Barnes and Co.
London: Thomas Yoseloff Ltd

©1968 by A.S. Barnes and Company, Inc.
Library of Congress Catalogue Card Number 68-11397

A.S. Barnes and Company, Inc.
Cranbury, New Jersey 08512

Thomas Yoseloff Ltd
108 New Bond Street
London W1Y OQX, England

First Printing March, 1968
Second Printing December, 1968
Third Printing March, 1971

ISBN: 0-498-06660-6
Printed in the United States of America

Dedicated To All
Horsemen

Contents

7

Introduction

There are more horses in the United States today than at any other time in history—a fact that may surprise some people. However, one fact I'm sure all horsemen are aware of is that each year there are fewer and fewer qualified horseshoers. A few decades ago, when the horse was the only means of transportation and the life blood for the human being, the people had to take good care of their horse's feet or they were left afoot. Now, with the shortage of farriers, people wait for weeks to have their horses shod. This condition prevails all over the country.

With that in mind, I write this book, hoping that you may find it of value, and that with some practice on your neighbor's horses you will be encouraged to shoe your own. Why do I say practice on your neighbor's horses? Just try shoeing your own horse, and within minutes your neighbor will be there volunteering his horses for you to do next. Try it and see.

The material in this book is the text I use in my horse-

9

shoeing class at the Utah Technical College at Provo, Utah. This school is one of the few in the United States offering a horseshoeing class as one of its regular night class programs. The class usually has a waiting list of students, which shows the demand for training in this field.

The book is an outgrowth of my search for materials suitable for instructing the art of horseshoeing. As most horse-lovers are aware, there is a shortage of printed matter on this subject. The text is not necessarily for the experienced horseshoer, although some may learn a great deal from reading it. It is primarily for the horse owner who wants to know more about his horse, how to go about shoeing it; and it is designed to help him appreciate the worth of such care. Let's not let horseshoeing become a lost art.

How to Shoe a Horse

Physiology of Legs and Feet

To understand the horse, you should be familiar with the physiology of its legs and feet. They are as important as are the wheels of an automobile. In fact, the legs and feet are the most important part of the horse as far as locomotion is concerned, and the horse is only as good as they are.

The skeleton of the horse's front legs is somewhat like the arm and hand of the human being, although the shoulder does not connect with the rest of the skeleton with bone, as it does in man. There is only a muscle connection. (*See Fig. 1.*)

a. ULNA and RADIUS: bones actually fused together, forming the elbow joint with the humerus.

b. CARPAL or KNEE: bones forming the wrist joint. There are two rows of bones, with either 3 or 4 to the row, depending on the horse. The action of the knee absorbs a great deal of shock.

13

Fig. 1—Physiology of the Legs and Feet

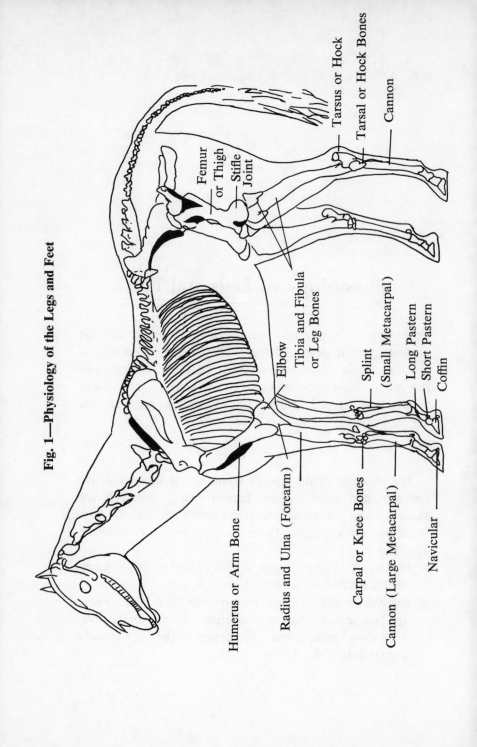

Femur or Thigh
Stifle Joint
Tarsus or Hock
Tarsal or Hock Bones
Cannon
Elbow
Tibia and Fibula or Leg Bones
Splint (Small Metacarpal)
Long Pastern
Short Pastern
Coffin
Humerus or Arm Bone
Radius and Ulna (Forearm)
Carpal or Knee Bones
Cannon (Large Metacarpal)
Navicular

c. CANNON: bone forming the fetlock joint with the long pastern. While it is exposed and subject to injury, the cannon is strong and seldom badly hurt.

d. The theory of evolution shows up in the horse; at one time he was probably a five-toed animal. Through the ages he lost all but the middle toe, and that is what he walks on today. The SPLINT bones, which attach at the top of the cannon and extend down about half way, are what remain of two of these toes. These bones give no apparent support; and on many horses become inflamed, causing a condition known as "splints." The CHESTNUT, located on the inside of the leg near the body, could be the remains of the big toe or thumb, and the ERGOT, the little toe or finger.

e. LONG or FIRST PASTERN: bone below the fetlock joint.

f. SHORT or SECOND PASTERN: bone connected to the long pastern at the pastern joint.

g. COFFIN: bone situated in the hoof, forming the coffin joint with the short pastern. These three bones (pastern and coffin) are like the bones in the finger of the human being.

The angle of these three bones to the rest of the horse's leg determines the type of pastern the horse has. If the angle is too steep, he will have a stumpy pastern. If the angle is too low, he will have a weak pastern. If the pastern is weak, leave the heel long and the toe short when horseshoeing; this will stand him up straighter. If the pastern is stumpy, lower the heel and leave the toe longer.

h. SESAMOID: small bone in back of the fetlock joint, a bearing surface for the flexor tendon.

HIND LEGS

The hind legs connect with the rest of the skeleton at the pelvis in the hip.

a. FEMUR: bone connecting at the pelvic joint.

b. PATELLA: bone called the stifle or stifle joint, similar to the human kneecap.

c. TIBIA: bone connecting the stifle to the hock. It has a small sliver of bone, called the FIBULA, which runs from the upper end down about half-way, similar to the splint bones.

d. HOCK: bone similar to the ankle of man. Like the front leg, it contains 7 or 8 bones, set in two layers. The larger of these extend upward in the back of the hock joint, where powerful tendons attach.

e. From here down the hind leg is much like the foreleg. The way in which these bones and joints are formed and the angles formed have a great deal to do with the way a horse moves. Faulty conformation causes interfering, forging, cross firing, and any number of malfunctions. Good, straight legs can take shock and produce much more power than crooked legs. Faulty conformation cannot be changed, but *corrective trimming and shoeing can help in many cases.*

FEET

Although we are concerned with the legs, we are more concerned with the feet. The feet are composed of four general classes of structures:

1. Bone
2. Elastic
3. Sensitive
4. Horn or Hoof

Bone. The bone structures of the feet consist of the long pastern, short pastern, coffin, and navicular bones (*Fig. 2*).

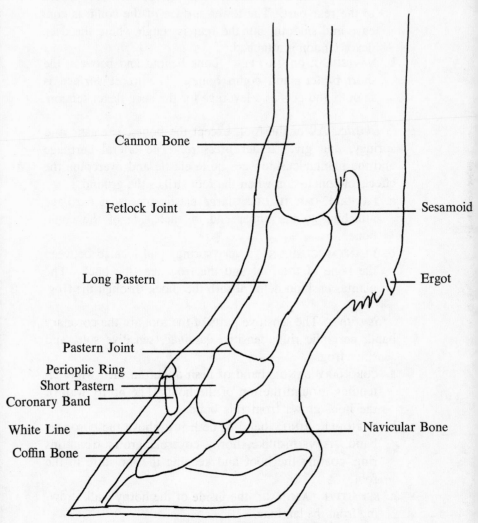

Fig. 2—The Main Parts of the Foot

a. COFFIN: wedge-shaped bone in the lower hoof. It has many small openings for blood and nerves, and the sensitive laminae are attached. The tendons of the foot attach to the coffin bone. The lateral cartilages attach to the rear part. The lower surface of the coffin is concave and smooth, but the rear is rough where the deep flexor tendon is attached.

b. NAVICULAR or SHUTTLE: bone behind and between the short pastern and coffin bones. The lower surface is smooth and acts as a leverage for the deep flexor tendon.

Elastic. All of the foot, except the bones, is elastic and springy, and gives under pressure. The lateral cartilage and the plantar cushion are quite elastic and overcome the effects of concussion when the foot strikes the ground.

a. LATERAL CARTILAGES: large elastic pieces of cartilage attaching to the upper end of each side of the coffin bone.

b. PLANTAR CUSHION: a very springy pad located between the bone of the foot and the frog near the back. The plantar cushion helps absorb the shock through the frog.

Sensitive. The sensitive parts of the foot are the coronary band, perioplic ring, sensitive laminae, sensitive sole, and sensitive frog.

a. CORONARY BAND: band of flesh about an inch wide extending around the top of the hoof. The horny wall of the hoof grows from this band.

b. PERIOPLIC RING: band of flesh just above the coronary band. A varnishlike, horny covering grows from this ring, coating the hoof and keeping the moisture in the foot.

c. SENSITIVE LAMINAE: the inside of the horny wall, growing from the laminae.

d. SENSITIVE SOLE: sensitive structure between the coffin bone and the horny sole. The horny sole grows from this sensitive sole.

e. SENSITIVE FROG: structure below the surface of the plantar cushion. The horny frog grows from this.

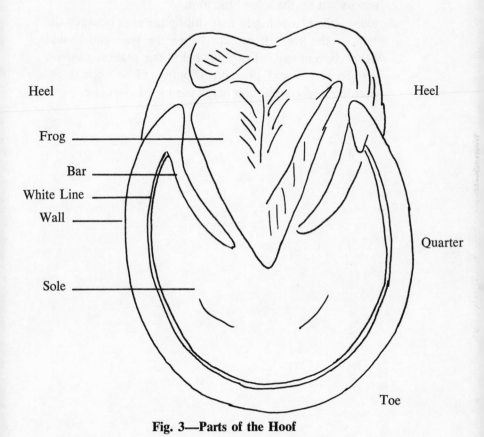

Fig. 3—Parts of the Hoof

Horn or Hoof. The hoof is divided into four parts: wall, bar, sole, and frog (*See Fig. 3*).

a. WALL: part extending from the hairline to the ground. The wall is divided into buttresses, quarter, and toe.

b. BAR: part extending inward from the wall to the point of the frog. The bar carries weight and also keeps the wall expanded.

c. HORNY SOLE: the sole of the foot.

d. FROG: the heart-shaped mass filling the area between the bars at the heel. It extends below the bars and should never be cut out. The frog helps the plantar cushion absorb shock and prevents slipping. The normal expansion and contraction helps the blood circulate.

Growth of the Hoof

The growth of the hoof depends upon the amount of blood supplied to the "quick." Good food, exercise, moisture, and the proper care of the hoof will cause rapid growth of horn of good quality. Lack of exercise, dryness, and excessive length of the hoof will hinder growth.

The average growth is about one-third inch per month. Hind hooves grow faster than forehooves, and unshod hooves normally grow faster than when they are shod.

The hoof, growing from the hairline down to form a completely new hoof, averages about eleven to thirteen months at the toe, six to eight months at the quarter, and three to five months at the heel. From this, we can estimate the time required for cracks, etc., to grow out.

Irregular growth is quite frequent. The cause is usually improper trimming, or no trimming at all. Colts running in soft pastures or confined to a stable for long periods of time are often neglected, and the hooves grow long and become dished out at the toe. The long quarters curl forward and inward and cause contraction of the heel; or the whole hoof bends outward or inward and a crooked foot, or even worse, a crooked leg results if this condition is allowed to exist for too long. Proper trimming of colts' hooves can partially correct crooked legs; on the other hand, improper trimming can cause crooked legs. It is much easier to prevent abnormalities than to correct them.

Horses running on hard, dry ground will wear their hooves gradually, and it will be necessary only to rasp them down from time to time, rounding off the sharp edges to prevent breaking and to keep the horses standing straight.

Foot Problems

Horses, like people, have foot problems. The following are a few of the most common problems the horseman should be aware of:

ACUTE FOUNDER OR LAMINITIS

Founder is an inflammation of the sensitive laminae and sensitive sole. In bad cases, it may involve still other parts of the internal foot. Causes for this ailment may be: eating too much of any kind of food; drinking lots of cold water when the body temperature is high; too much oats, rye, or wheat; overexertion on hard roads; bruises; punctures; faulty shoeing; nail pricks when shoeing; or it may appear without any apparent cause.

Founder is generally found in the front feet, rarely in the rear. When both front feet are affected, which they generally are, the horse will put its hind feet under the body in order to relieve the weight on the front feet. In bad cases the animal will want to lie down to ease the pressure on the feet.

The breathing is fast and heavy, the pulse is rapid and strong, and the hoof will be hot. If the foot is tapped lightly, the horse will evince great pain. The horse will rest better lying down in a clean bed of straw. It is generally a good practice to bathe the foot with warm water for some time, then change to cold water. Keep this up until the swelling goes down. If you suspect founder, call your veterinarian.

THRUSH

Thrush is a disease of the feet involving the soft parts of the hoof, principally the frog. This is usually caused by unsanitary conditions in the stall where a horse must stand for prolonged periods in manure and urine-soaked bedding, etc. Prolonged work on muddy roads and neglected shoeing are contributing factors.

Thrush is characterized by a discharge of dark, foulsmelling matter from the frog. The hoof and heel are hot to the touch, and the horse may become lame, especially on hard, rough surfaces or when striking hard objects.

In treating thrush, the loose and diseased tissue in the wall, frog, and sole should be cut away; but be very careful to avoid bleeding. Clean the hoof with warm water and soap, then apply a disinfectant, making sure that it covers all the infected area, especially the bottom of the crevices. Pack the clefts of the frog with oakum saturated with disinfectant, using a leather pad under the shoe. Keep the horse in a dry, clean place.

FLAT FOOT

Flat foot is a condition where the sole has very little

convexity. This problem is confined to forefeet that usually are broad, low heeled, and with walls that are not upright, as seen in good feet. The entire weight of the animal rests on the plantar surface. Horses with flat feet are more susceptible to bruises and corns and lose their shoes easily. They should be shod with a shoe having a wide web pressing on the wall only. Never pare the heel or frog.

CLUBFOOT

Clubfoot is a term applied to feet when the walls are set nearly perpendicular. The heels are high, the fetlock joint is thrown forward, and the weight of the animal is received on the toe. In severe cases clubfoot may be cured by cutting the tendon, but as a rule, special shoeing is the only measure of relief. The toe should be left long and the heel lowered as much as possible, setting the shoe as far forward as you can and still supporting the wall of the hoof with the shoe.

QUARTER, SAND, AND TOE CRACKS

Quarter and sand cracks usually appear on the upper part of the hoof, where the wall is thin. The cracks usually appear because of the dry and brittle condition of the hoof or outside shell.

When the weight is thrown upon the foot, these cracks will open, and then close when the weight is released. When the crack is open, the sensitive tissue will get into the crack and be pinched on the release of the weight. This will cause irritation, inflammation, and great lameness.

When these conditions occur, poultice the foot or bathe it in warm water, using about 1/2 teaspoonful of carbolic acid to a bucket of water.

When the foot is free from exposed tissue and the fever

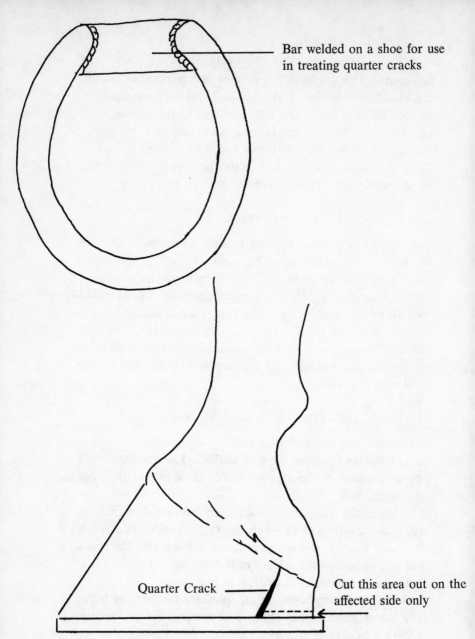

Bar welded on a shoe for use in treating quarter cracks

Quarter Crack

Cut this area out on the affected side only

Fig. 4—Shoeing for Quarter Cracks

For quarter cracks cut out the area of the hoof as shown and shoe with a barred shoe. This will keep the crack from spreading and will relieve the pressure from the affected area.

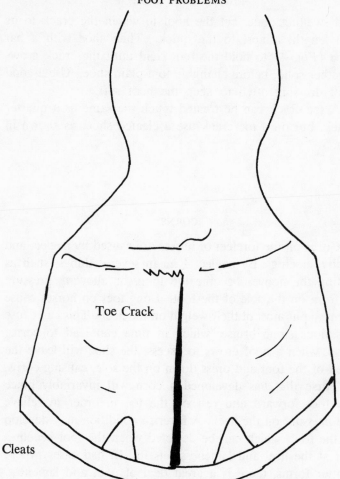

Toe Crack

Cleats

Fig. 5—Shoeing for Toe Cracks

To stop a toe crack from spreading use a shoe with two cleats on the front. You will have to cut small holes in the hoof wall for the cleats to fit in.

and swelling gone, cut the hoof to widen the crack to its full length, almost to the quick. Then shoe with a bar shoe (*Fig. 4*) to hold the foot rigid until the crack grows together solid, before changing to a plain shoe. Use a good hoof dressing often to keep the hoof soft.

A toe crack can be treated much the same as a quarter crack, but on a toe crack use a cleated shoe, as shown in Fig. 5.

CORNS

Corns on the forefeet of horses are caused by neglect and faulty shoeing. By neglect I mean several things, such as letting the hooves become too long, or allowing pressure to form on the sole of the foot. Long toes on horses cause them to put most of their weight on the heels. This can cause a serious stone bruise, which in time can lead to corns. Also, when a hoof grows to excess, the shoe will leave the shell of the foot and press down on the sole, causing corns. A horse that has developed a corn will invariably place the foot forward and rest on the toe in order to relieve the pressure on the heel. A feverish condition may develop in the foot, which can be detected when the foot becomes hot at the heel and lameness sets in. In bad cases, where matter forms, there is a great deal of pain and lameness. The matter may travel up inside the hard shell, then fester, and eventually break the skin at the top of the hoof in order to relieve the pressure and release the pus. If the shoe is the cause, removing it will usually be all that is necessary. If it is caused by a bruise, the sole over the corn should be removed to let the infected area drain. Then treat as a wound.

GRAVEL

Gravel in a foot is generally caused by a small rock or pebble pressing through the outer shell of the sole of the foot. Once the stone is through the shell, the foot will quickly grow over the hole, leaving the stone to fester and seek a way out. After fever sets in, the stone will follow the path of least resistance, which is generally up inside the shell until it reaches the hairline. There it will fever and fester, the same way a bad sliver will fester in a human being. A poultice or hot pack will usually relieve the pain.

The Shoe

The shoe is an artificial base of support, by no means ideal because it interferes to a greater or lesser degree with the physiology of the foot. But it is indispensable, except for horses at slow work on soft ground.[1]

The shoe should be selected for the type of work the horse is to do, unless you are trying to correct a foot with a special type of shoe.

If you make your own shoes, you can make them to suit your own needs; but as most people buy their shoes ready-made, they can select the shoe that fits the type of work the horse is required to do. For most horses in this area, the plane shoe, or plate (*Figs. 6 and 29*) as it is called, is the most widely used, especially in the arena, where horses are required to stop and turn fast. Shoes with small heel and toe calks are popular with horsemen who use their steeds in the mountains and rocks. These small calks give the horses better footing and a little more wear to the shoes.

---

[1] Leonard Pearson, and others, *Diseases of the Horse* (Washington, D.C.: Government Printing Office, 1911), p. 578.

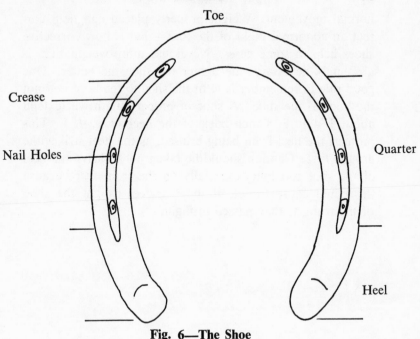

Fig. 6—The Shoe

It has been my experience that the "heel and toe" shoe is not good for arena horses because of the drag that they cause on a horse as he stops. It seems to hurt when they slide, and as most people know who have seen good working horses work, a good slide is very important. The slide is especially important to the calf-roping horse as this helps to relieve the shock placed on the horse as the running calf hits the end of the rope. Calked shoes can also be dangerous when riding on a hard surface. The horse is then forced to stand up on three points. This causes a loss of friction on the shoe and eliminates all possible chances of the frog acting as it is intended to act.

The weight of the shoe is very important because any added weight to the hoof makes the foot exaggerate its normal movement. Weight properly placed can help correct an abnormal flight of the foot—that is how corrective shoes help in some cases. Never use more weight than is absolutely necessary; the lighter the shoe the better. One good rule to remember is to fit the shoe to the hoof and not the hoof to the shoe. A shoe of proper length will extend about 1/4 to 3/8 inch back of the heel (*Fig. 48*). This protects the heel from being bruised, as the heel strikes the ground first. Caution should be taken not to leave the heel of the shoe too long, especially on the front feet because this could cause trouble if the rear feet caught the shoe of the front as they passed in flight.

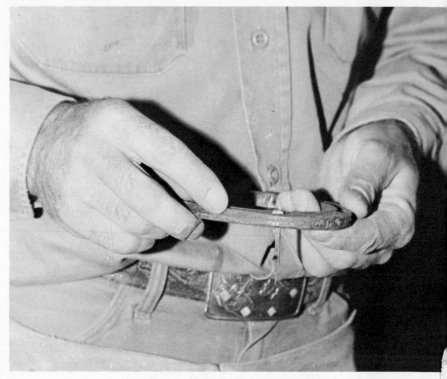

Fig. 7—The Head of the Nail

For a proper fit, the head of the nail should fit well down into the shoe. This will prevent the head from being worn off and the shoe lost.

about catching onto the feel; it will be much easier after you have driven several boxes of nails.

The number 5 city head is good for shoes 00 through 1. If you need shoes larger than this, use a bigger nail. If you are using race plates or polo plates, then you will have to use a much smaller nail. These smaller nails are also availble. Usually you can buy shoes and nails where "tack" is sold.

The Nail

Care should be taken to select the proper nail for the shoe to be used. There is a good variety of horseshoe nails on the market today, so you have a good selection. I have found that for the type of shoeing I do the number 5 city head does the best job. It is important that the head of the nail be set well down into the hole of the shoe (*Fig. 7*). If the nail is too large, the head will soon wear off and the shoe will then be easily thrown. If, on the other hand, the nail is too small, the shoe will soon become loose and will be lost. Figure 8(c) shows that the pointed end of the nail is beveled on the inside. This is so the nail will have a tendency to angle out of the hoof as it is driven in. But be careful—even though they are beveled, they will still try to follow the grain of the hoof and you may prick the sensitive part of the foot. If this happens, be sure to disinfect the hole and call your veterinarian for a tetanus shot.

The inside of the nail has crisscross markings. This is so you can tell the different sides by the feel. Don't worry

33

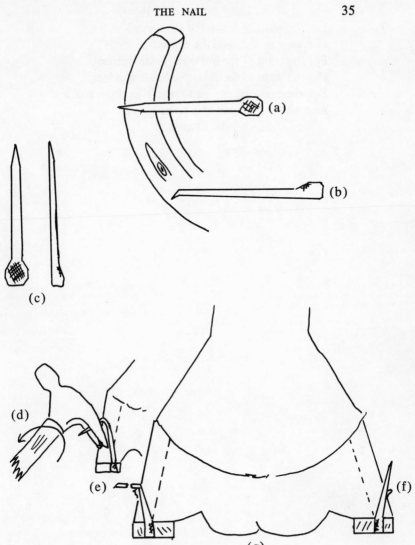

Fig. 8—Handling the Nail

For the want of a nail the shoe was lost,
For want of the shoe the horse was lost,
For the want of the horse the rider was lost,
For the want of the rider the battle was lost,
For the want of the battle the Kingdom was lost—
And all for the want of a horseshoe-nail.

BENJAMIN FRANKLIN

Shoeing Chaps

The person who shoes a horse without some kind of protection on his legs is very foolish. No matter how gentle the horse may be, he will jump or jerk if the right situation arises. The point of the horseshoe nail is very sharp and could cut deep into the leg if the horse jerked at the wrong time. Even with chaps on you could be hurt, but the chances would be less.

I call the design of chaps I use the "'Utah Chaps" (*See Fig. 9*), because of the shape of each leg leather. You will notice that they are shaped like the outline of the state of Utah.

You could make a pair of these chaps in a couple of hours and for about six dollars. I made mine out of split leather. After cutting the two leg pieces (*Fig. 9*), I laced them together with a leather string (*Fig. 10*).

Notice that I have used only one small rivet on each strap, and that the straps are made from strips of the same leather, one-half-inch wide. This is so they will give and pull apart if by some chance the horse gets his foot caught in the chaps.

Always think safety when around a horse.

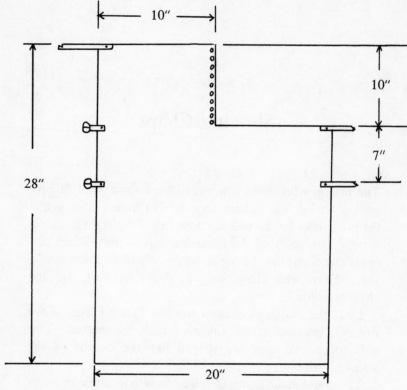

Fig. 9—The Shoeing Chap

One side of the Utah shoeing chap. The other side is cut the same size and shape but then turned over and laced together as shown in Fig. 10.

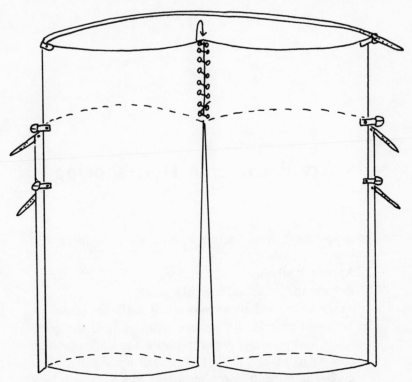

Fig. 10—The Shoeing Chaps Laced Together

The Utah shoeing chap. Split grain leather is good. Straps are also made from the same leather. Buckles or snaps can be used.

Safety Practices in Horseshoeing

1. If you don't know the horse, have someone there with you.
2. Approach all horses with caution.
3. Respect the horse and treat him gently.
4. Never make sudden moves that will startle the horse.
5. To avoid trouble, either have someone hold the horse or tie him securely, preferably with the lead-rope high enough to make him hold his head up slightly. This makes it difficult for him to do much except look straight ahead.
6. Never tie a horse with a rope long enough for him to step over it.
7. Always use a good, strong halter, not just a rope around the neck.
8. Wear a leather apron or chaps to keep your legs and trousers from being harmed.
9. Always twist off the nails as soon as they are driven in.
10. Try not to let the horse jerk away. This will not only

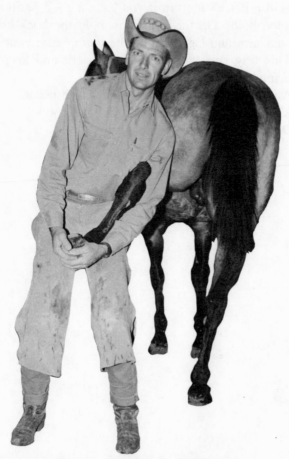

Fig. 11—Holding the Hind Foot

To hold the hind foot of a horse that starts to jerk and fuss, hold the lower leg as shown and bend the toe up. If you will hang on and not let go, you can hold the foot up without getting hurt.

develop into a bad habit, but it is dangerous. You can hold a horse's foot up if you have a good position and good hold. On the hind foot, hold the hock between your arm and leg, bending the toe up with your hand. This way you can ride with the jerk and keep from being kicked. (*See Fig. 11.*)

11. Always work on a flat area, clear of obstacles.
12. Keep tool box and equipment out of the way.
13. Don't swallow the horseshoe nails!

Horseshoeing Tools

Figure 12 shows all the tools you will ever need to shoe a horse with the exception of the anvil and shoeing chaps, which are shown in Figs. 27 and 9.

No. 14 is a large hammer for shaping the shoes.

No. 15 is the shoeing hammer. The slit between the claws is designed for twisting off the ends of the nails (*Fig. 8*).

No. 16 is a tang rasp. Use the smoother side for removing the clinches and the rougher side for rasping the hoof. The handle usually is sold separately.

No. 17 is a pair of horseshoe pincers, used for cutting nails, etc., and for removing the old shoes.

No. 18 is an expensive pair of hoof nippers. The regular, less-expensive nippers (called parers) are larger, and one side is a cutting blade while the other side is blunt.

No. 19 is a hand clincher bar.

No. 21 is the clinching pliers, called clinchers.

43

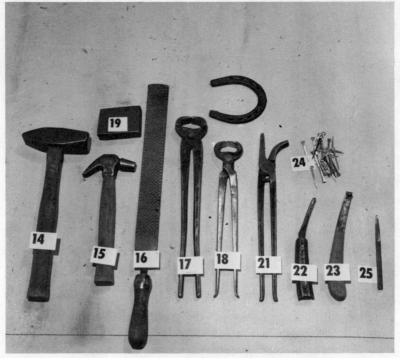

Fig. 12—Tools You Will Need to Shoe a Horse

These tools can be purchased from almost any hardware store or western shop. They should not cost much over $40 at the most.

No. 22 is a metal-handled hoof knife with a removable blade.

No. 23 is a wooden-handled knife. It comes either left or right handed.

No. 25 is a pritchel, used to enlarge the nail holes in the shoes.

Examination of the Hoof
Before Shoeing

The object of an examination of the hoof before shoeing is to ascertain the following:

    a. The direction and position of the limbs.

    b. The shape and quality of the hooves.

    c. The position and wear of the shoes. (*See Fig. 13.*)

    d. The manner in which the hooves leave the ground.

    e. The hooves' line of flight.

    f. The way the hooves are set on the ground.

    g. Any other peculiarities.

From the above examination we will know how to properly prepare the hooves for correct shoeing.

We must, therefore, observe the horse both at rest and in motion. First, stand in front and observe the way the horse stands. Are his feet straight, or do they angle in or out? If they point out, this is called base-wide. If they point in, this is called base-narrow. If they are extremely wide, they are called splay-footed. If they are extremely narrow, they are called pigeon-toed.

Next, stand to the side and observe the angle of the pastern. This angle should be nearly 45 degrees. The angle may vary slightly but should be kept as near to this as possible. (*See Fig. 16.*)

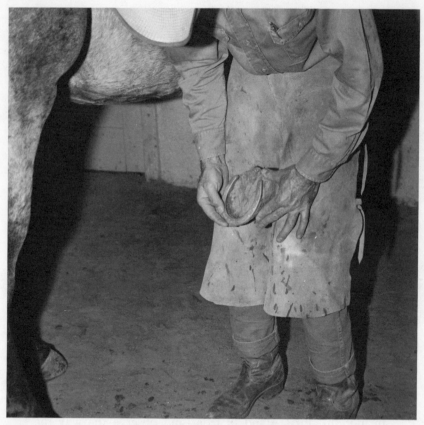

Fig. 13—Examining the Old Shoe

Before you remove the old shoe, check the way it wore. You can tell how the foot broke over by the way the shoe wore.

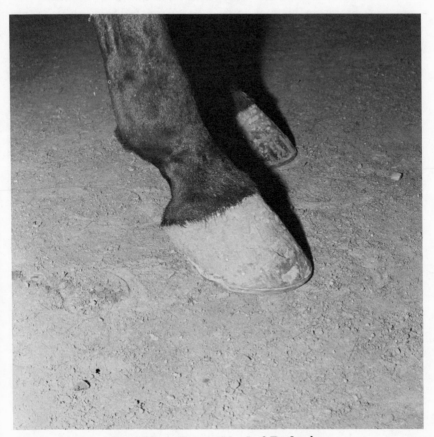

Fig. 14—A Foot in Need of Reshoeing

This photo shows a foot well in need of being reshod. Note the extra length of the hoof. Also note the damaged area near the toe. When this hoof is properly trimmed and re-shod, the damaged area will be removed.

Finally, observe the horse at a walk and a trot. Watch how he places his feet. See if he swings his forefeet as he moves, and if he overreaches or interferes.

Before you even try to pick up a horse's foot, pet him around the head and neck. Let him get to know you by smelling your hands. If you are calm and unafraid of him,

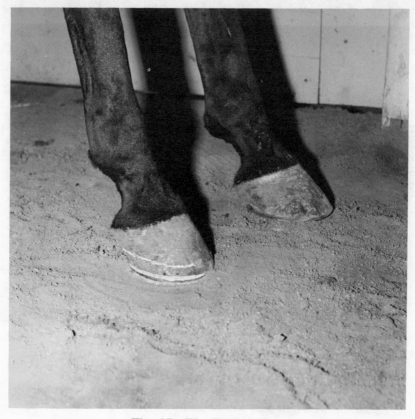

Fig. 15—The Reshod Foot

The nearest foot has now been reshod. The chalk line shows the area where the nails should come out and be clinched.

he will know this by smelling and he will stand much better for you while you work on him.

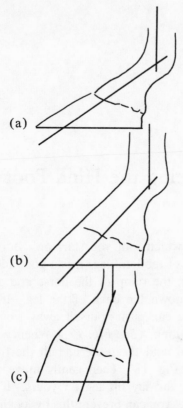

Fig. 16—Angle of the Pastern

(a) This foot and pastern are on less than a 45 degree angle and the pastern is weak.

(b) This angle is nearly correct on a 45 degree angle.

(c) This angle is too steep and the foot is stumpy.

Shoeing the Hind Foot

It doesn't matter which foot you start on. But when you go to pick up one of the hind legs it is a good idea to place your free hand on the rump of the horse and gently slide your other hand down the back of the leg. If he should kick or jump, you can push yourself away from him with the hand on the rump. (*See Fig. 17.*) When you get your hand down and around the pastern, pull the foot up and out, as shown in Fig. 18. Then gently move toward the rear of the horse and lay his leg on yours. If he should want to jerk a little, you can prevent this by locking his hock under your inside arm and pulling up on the toe of his foot, as shown in Fig. 11.

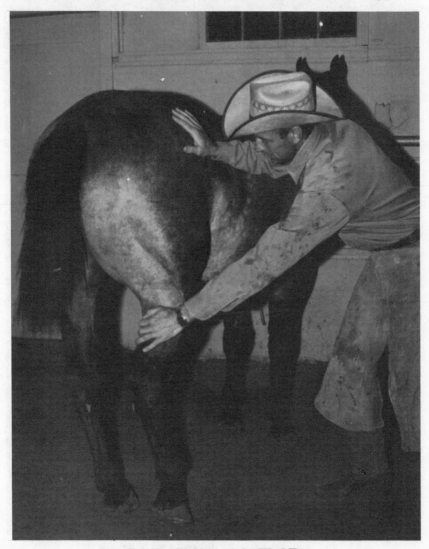

Fig. 17—Picking up the Hind Feet

Most people are afraid to pick up the hind feet for fear of being kicked. If you are careful and do as I have directed you will be surprised how easy it is.

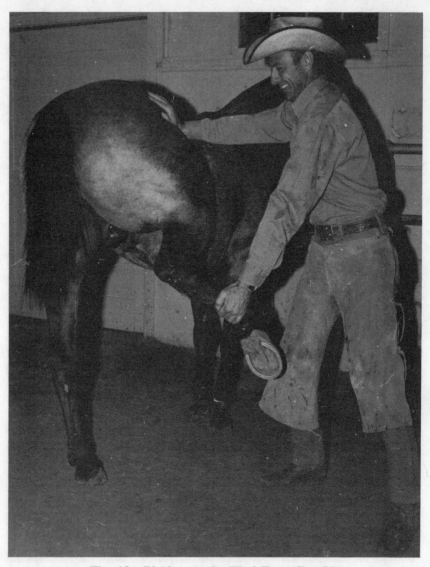

Fig. 18—Picking up the Hind Feet (Contd.)

After you have run your hand down the leg as shown in Fig. 17, lift the leg up and out. Then remove your right hand from the hip and grab the leg on the hock, as you walk to the rear and under the leg. Lay the foot in your lap with your legs tight together.

Removing the Shoe

To remove the old shoe, place the foot on your knee as shown in Fig. 19, and remove the old clinch with the back or smoother side of your rasp. With the clinch gone, the old nail will pull freely through the hoof without damaging the wall. Then move back to the rear position, and using the pincers as shown in Fig. 20, pry the heel of the shoe up. Work from side to side toward the toe until the shoe is off.

Remove the old shoe and pincers from the area so you won't have them to fall over.

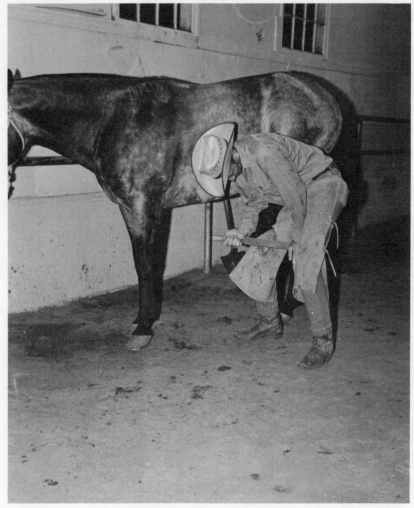

Fig. 19—Removing the Clinch

To remove the old clinch before removing the shoe, place the foot on your knee as shown, and using the smoother side of the rasp, file away the clinched end of the nail.

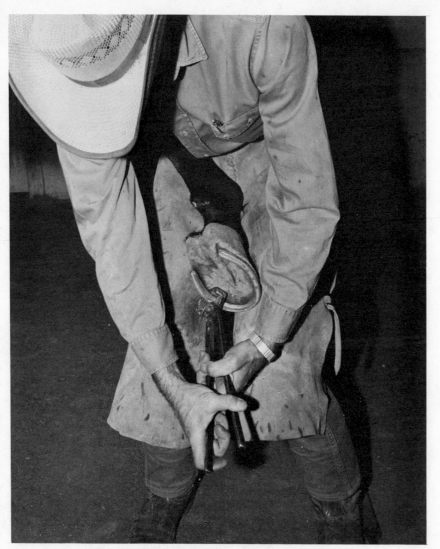

Fig. 20—Removing the Old Shoe

After the clinch has been removed (Fig. 19), the old shoe can easily be removed with your pincers as shown. Start at the heel and work toward the toe.

Preparing the Foot for the Shoe

After the old shoe is removed, you are ready to prepare the foot for the new shoe. Start by examining the foot. Clean the frog and check for thrush and corns (*Fig. 21*).

Next, holding your nippers square with the foot, start the cut at the toe (*Fig. 22*). Cut about as deep as the photo shows (*Fig. 22*) from the toe around to one side and then back to the toe and around to the other side. Be careful in this first cutting not to cut too deeply. To avoid getting the heel too low, make your cut angle from where you start at the toe, to nothing at the heel (*Figs. 23 and 24*). Then if you see that you still have too much hoof, repeat the procedure.

Most people have the idea that the frog should be cut away, but this is definitely wrong. The frog is there for a very definite purpose and must not be cut at all.

Now you are ready for rasping. Don't be too discouraged if at first you have trouble making the rasp cut smoothly. The secret to rasping is the amount of pressure applied.

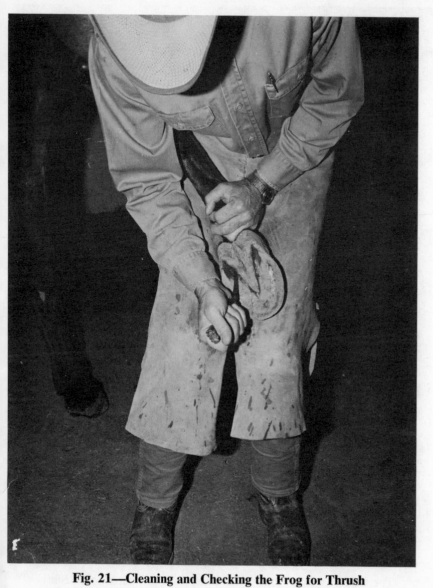

Fig. 21—Cleaning and Checking the Frog for Thrush

After the shoe has been removed, the crevices of the frog should be cleaned and the frog checked for thrush. *Never cut away the frog.* Trim the dead ends and overgrown areas, but leave the rest of the frog intact.

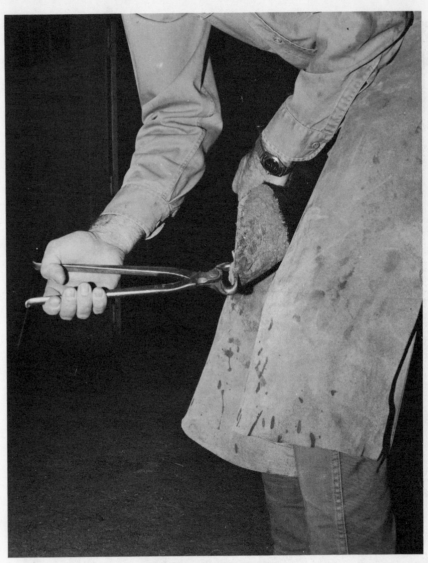

Fig. 22—Paring the Hoof

The excessive hoof can be cut away with the parer tool. Start at the toe and work toward the heel. Make your cut so it angles out to nothing at the heel (See Figs. 23 and 24). If you will do this, you will not end up with low heels as so many shoers do.

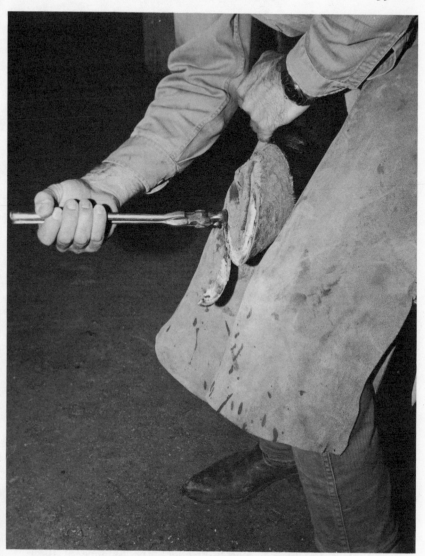

Fig. 23—Paring the Hoof (Contd.)

End up with nothing at the heel, as shown.

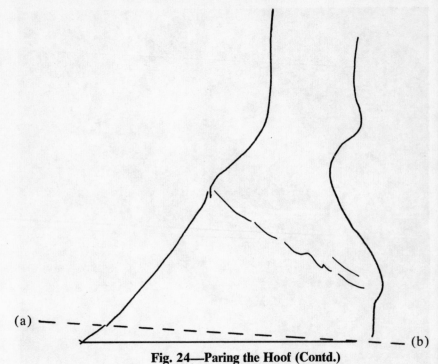

Fig. 24—Paring the Hoof (Contd.)

When nipping the hoof, cut as shown from (a) to (b).

Make long, smooth strokes like you were sawing a board with a good handsaw. Note Figs. 25 and 26. See how I am holding the rasp? Note also the way the foot is lying in my lap. Cut from the heel down, using the heel only as a guide. The wall of the heel is very thin and will cut much faster than the rest of the foot, so be careful not to cut it as fast as the toe.

Now is the time to carefully check the balance of the foot. Push the toe down so you can sight across the whole foot, making sure that the foot is level. Make sure also

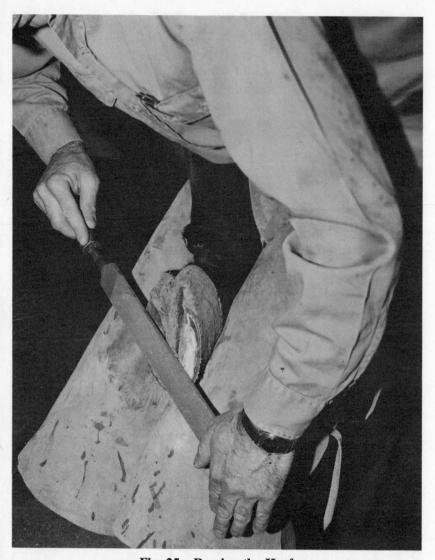

Fig. 25—Rasping the Hoof

Rasp from the heel to the toe, using the heel only as a guide. The wall at the heel is very thin and will rasp away much faster than the toe.

that the foot is the same height on both sides. This is extremely important. (*See Fig. 47.*)

As you rasp, be careful to watch the color of the sole. When it becomes pinkish at the toe, you are deep enough.

Fig. 26—Rasping the Hoof (Contd.)
Hold the rasp as shown and make long, smooth strokes.

After the shoe has been spread to the desired width, place the ends of the shoe through the hole as shown in Fig. 28(b) and bend the ends around so they will follow the outline of the foot. If you will notice the shoes in Fig. 29, you will see that the shoe numbered 15 is almost round,

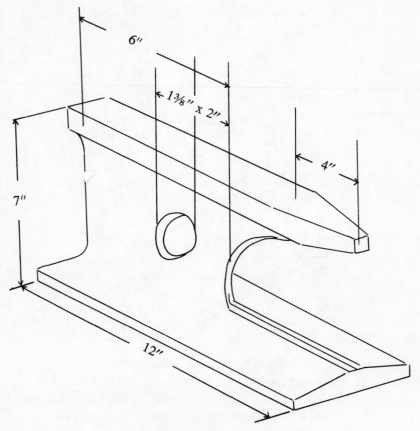

Fig. 27—Building an Anvil

An inexpensive anvil made from a piece of railroad rail.

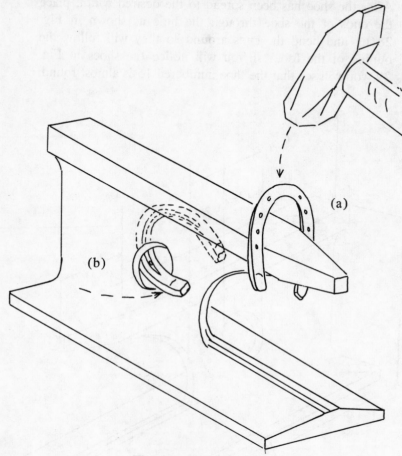

Fig. 28—Shaping a Shoe

(a) To spread a shoe.

(b) To bend the ends around to fit the heel on the foot.

while the shoe numbered 14 is oblong. Number 15 will fit a front foot and the heels of the shoe will be well under the hoof where it will protect the heels but will not be stepped on by the hind feet. Figs. 30 and 31 show how to make a shoe elongated to fit the hind feet of your horse. Most horses today have round feet on the front and oblong feet on the back. Lay the shoe on the anvil as shown and hit it near where the toe and quarter meet. After both sides have been sprung out as Fig. 30(b) shows, then bring the heels back together as shown in Fig. 31(b). Then turn the ends, using the hole, so they will look like Fig. 31(c).

After the shoe has been shaped to fit the foot, turn the anvil upside down, as shown in Fig. 32, and flatten the shoe with your hammer. Making sure the shoe is flat is very important. If it is not flat, it will not lie smoothly on the foot.

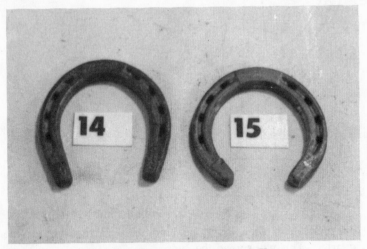

Fig. 29—Shaped and Unshaped Shoes

Shoe No. 14 is as it comes from the factory. Shoe No. 15 has been shaped to fit a front foot. Note that it is almost round.

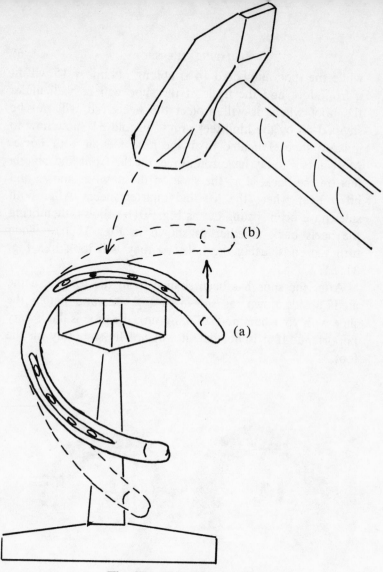

(b)

(a)

Fig. 30—Elongating the Shoe

To elongate a shoe to fit the hind feet, hit the shoe at the
quarter. This will spread the ends.

After the shoe has been shaped to the foot and has been leveled, place it on the hoof as shown in Figs. 33 and 34. It is very important that the shoe be set well up on the toe of the foot. Use your finger as shown in Fig. 34 to get the

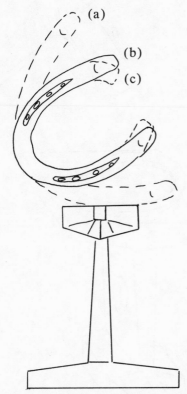

Fig. 31—Elongating the Shoe for Hind Foot

After the shoe has been spread, it should then be narrowed by hitting the ends, first on one side and then on the other. Then the ends should be bent in as shown in (c) to follow the outline of the hoof.

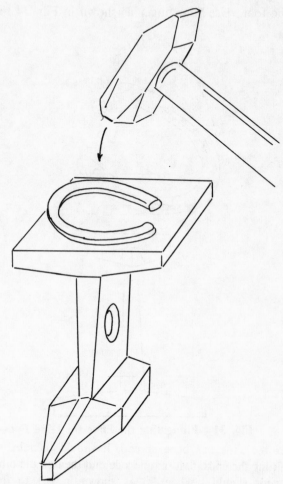

Fig. 32—Flattening the Shoe

After the shoe has been *shaped to fit the foot,* the anvil should be turned over and the shoe tapped on until the shoe is flat.

shoe where it belongs. Many shoers let the shoe set back from the toe and end up with the foot dubbed off (that is, the toe cut off to fit the shoe). This not only looks bad but causes the foot to break over sooner than it is supposed to. SET THE SHOE RIGHT UP FLUSH WITH THE TOE.

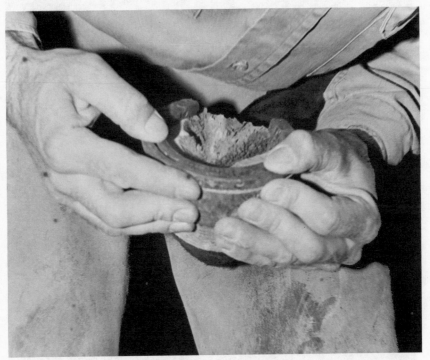

Fig. 33—Setting the Shoe

The shoe should fit well upon the toe for a good fit. Never set the shoe back and dub off the toe.

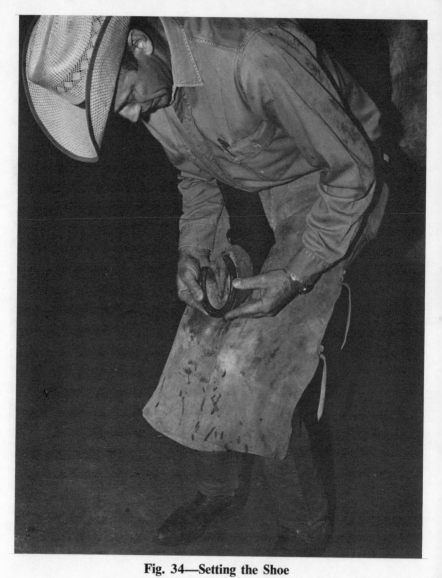

Fig. 34—Setting the Shoe

This, like Fig. 33, shows how the shoe should be set on the
hoof before the nails are driven.

Driving the Nail

A good way to start the first nail is as shown in Figs. 35 and 36. Place the shoe smooth with the outer edge of the hoof, making sure that it is well upon the toe (*Fig. 34*).

Start the first nail in the first hole toward the horse. Put the point of the nail in the inside outer corner of the hole and push it into the horn with your hand. Then stand the nail up straight and pound in (*Fig. 36*). Do the same with the other front hole. Then continue from front to back.

When you are ready to drive the last nail on both sides, bend the tip of the nail as shown in Fig. 37, and Fig. 8 (a) and (b). After bending the tip of the nails as shown, drive them.

If any of the nails have not broken through the surface of the hoof wall by the time they are halfway in, pull them out and change the angle of the nail. The same holds true if the nail comes out too quickly.

To avoid driving a nail in an old hole, change the angle up or down from the long way of the foot.

The reason for bending the tip of the last two nails is to make them come out quicker. (The wall of the hoof at the heel is much steeper than at the toe and quarter.)

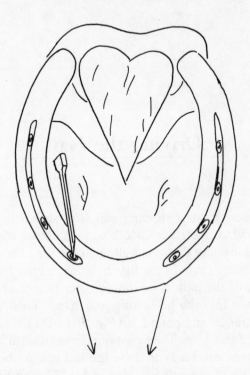

Fig. 35—Starting the First Nail

To start the first nail, make sure the shoe is flush with the toe. Place the nail in the front hole with the point in the corner of the hole as shown and then after pressing the nail into the hoof with your finger, stand it up and drive it in. This will force the shoe ahead a little; but after the other front and the rest of the nails have been driven, the shoe will be up on the toe where it belongs. Don't let the shoe slip back. If it does, take it off and start over.

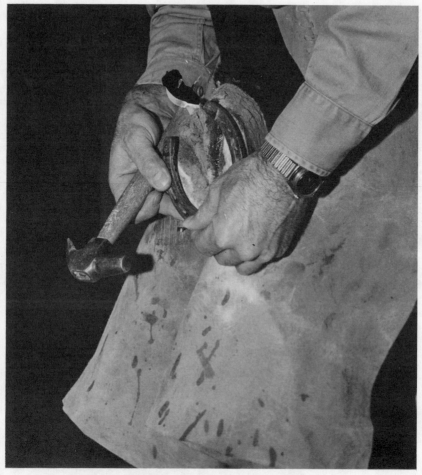

Fig. 36—Starting the First Nail

To keep the shoe from slipping back when you drive the nails, start the first nail as shown. See also Fig. 35.

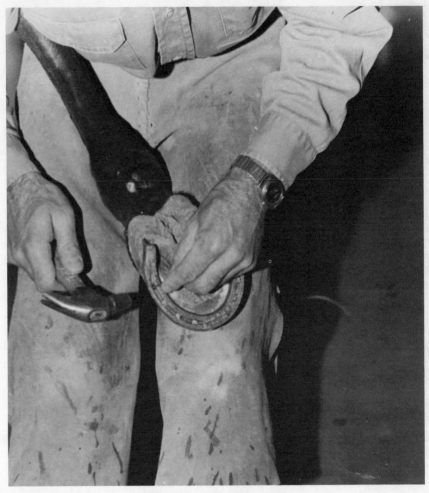

Fig. 37—The Rear Nails

Before starting the last two nails, bend the tip as shown.
Also see Fig. 8, Nos. (a) and (b).

Fig. 38—The Pants Cuff as a Nail Pouch

A turned-up cuff makes a very good pocket to keep your horseshoe nails in while you are shoeing. In the other cuff place the ends of the nails as you twist them off. Then when you are through shoeing, you can dispose of them all at once where your horse or car tires won't pick them up.

The Clinch

Getting a good clinch is very important, for the shoe will stay on only as long as the clinch is good (*Fig. 39*).

After the nail has been driven through the wall of the hoof, it should be bent to a right angle and twisted off. See Fig. 8 (d).

When all of the nails have been driven and twisted off, the burr under the twisted end (*Fig. 8[f]*) should be rasped away, using the smoother side of the rasp (*Fig. 40*).

Now the nail should be clinched (*Fig. 39*). This can be done either with a bar, as shown in Fig. 41, or with a pair of clinchers, as shown in Fig. 42.

Be careful not to get the clinch too tight. If you do, this can cause the horse to become lame. On the other hand, too loose a clinch will cause a loose shoe, and a loose shoe is easily thrown.

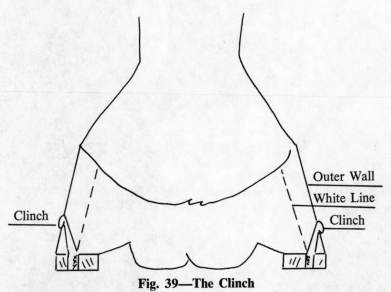

Outer Wall

White Line

Clinch

Clinch

Fig. 39—The Clinch

After the nail is driven, twisted off and the burr under it removed, then the clinch can be made. The better the clinch, the longer the shoe will stay on.

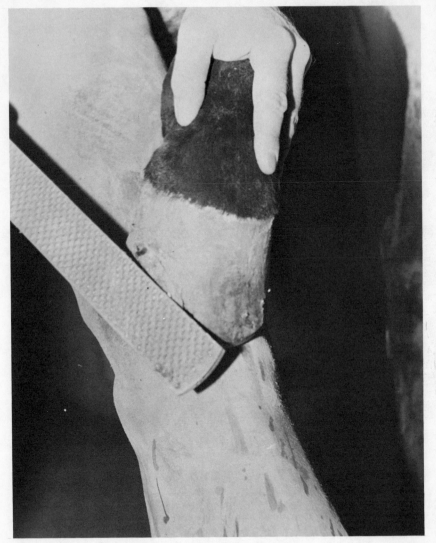

Fig. 40—Removing the Burr

After the nail has been driven and the end twisted off, the burr
under the nail should be removed.

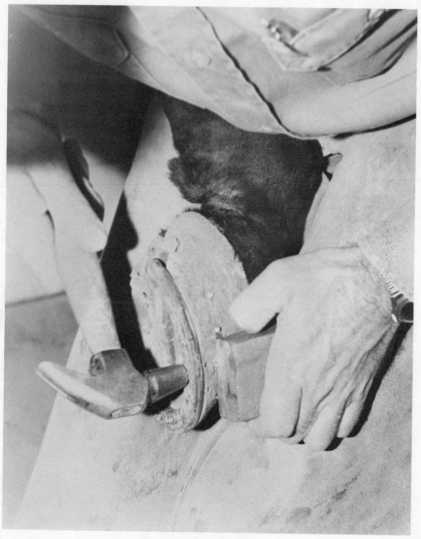

Fig. 41—The Bar Clinch

One way to clinch the nail is as shown. Any metal bar, or the head of your pincers can be used. Place the bar under the nail and pound on the head of the nail. This will clinch the end.

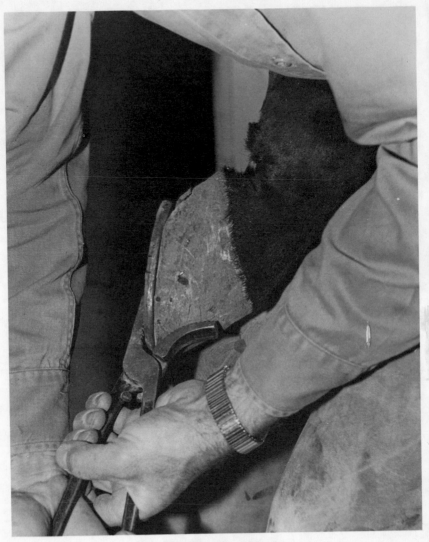

Fig. 42—The Plier Clincher

This special tool does a very good job of clinching, but it takes a while to learn how to use it.

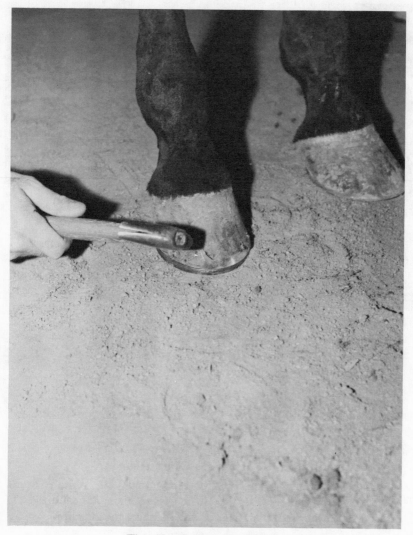

Fig. 43—Setting the Clinch

After the nail has been clinched, set the foot down and gently tap the clinch into the hoof wall. This will set the clinch and you will be surprised how much better the job will look and how much longer the shoe will remain tight. If the horse won't stand while you do this tapping, have someone hold the other leg off the ground, or set the foot you are working on up on your knee by pulling the leg forward.

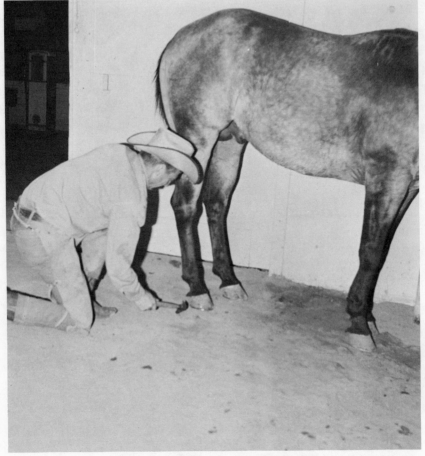

Fig. 44—Setting the Clinch (Contd.)

When working in this position, be careful and alert. Place your left hand on the horse's stifle. If he tries to kick, you can push yourself away from him. This is while tapping the clinches.

Shoeing the Front Foot

The front leg is easy to pick up if you take your thumb and first finger and gently squeeze the tendon back of the cannon bone as shown in Fig. 45. He will usually take the weight off that leg, and you can then pull the foot up. Place the lower leg of the horse between your legs, just above the knee, and apply pressure which will hold the leg up. If you take a half-step toward the rear of the horse so you are in the position shown in Fig. 46, the horse will be more relaxed and it will be easier to work on him. Also if you stay out away from the horse as far as you can and still hold onto the leg, you will have more freedom to work. As you work on the foot you should tilt the hoof down with both hands and make sure that you keep the hoof level. Fig. 47.

If the horse should want to fight you while working on the front feet, reach up with the arm closest to him, lay it over his neck, and hold on. Usually after a few tries he will settle down and you will be able to work on him. Horses that have the habit of rearing back when they are tied up will bear watching as you shoe the front feet. This can be very dangerous because, as he goes back, he usually pulls you back with him. If he is one that likes to take his

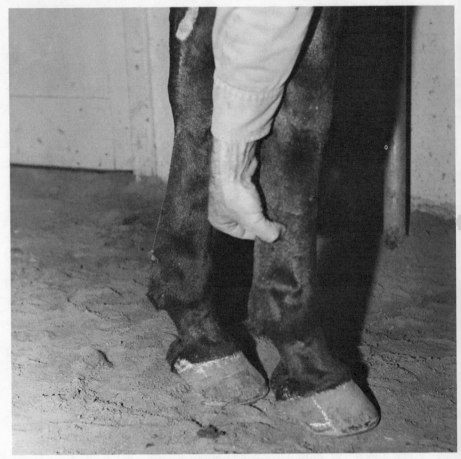

Fig. 45—Raising the Front Foot

To raise the front foot, grasp the tendon as shown with the first finger and thumb. Apply pressure until the horse lifts the foot. Then catch the pastern and straddle the leg.

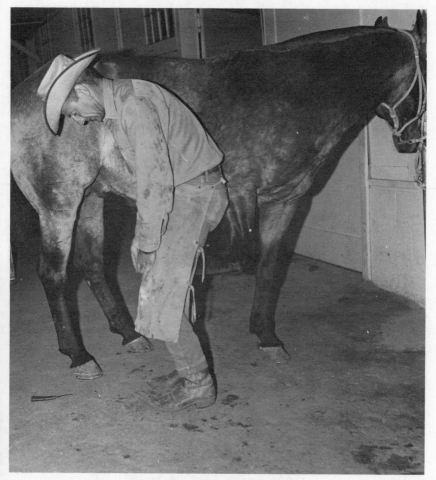

Fig. 46—Holding the Front Leg

By holding the front leg as shown, with the upper part of the leg straight up and down and the lower leg parallel with the ground, the horse and you will be more comfortable. Don't stay close to the horse. Keep as much working area between you and the horse as you can by stepping out from him.

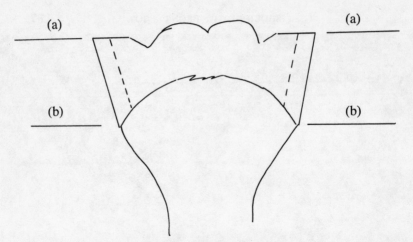

Fig. 47—A Balanced Foot

Make sure the area between (a) and (b) is the same. This is the only way you will be able to keep the hoof level.

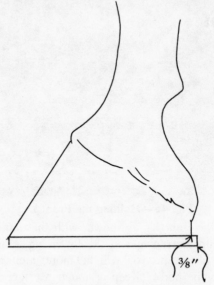

Fig. 48—Proper Length of Shoe

The shoe should extend at least ¼″ but not over ⅜″ as shown.

foot whenever he feels like it, you should try very hard to prevent this, as it will become a very bad habit if you continue letting him get away with it.

When you shape the front shoes, be sure that you get the heels of the shoe under the heels of the feet, and not have them extended more than one-fourth inch back of the feet. Refer to Fig. 48.

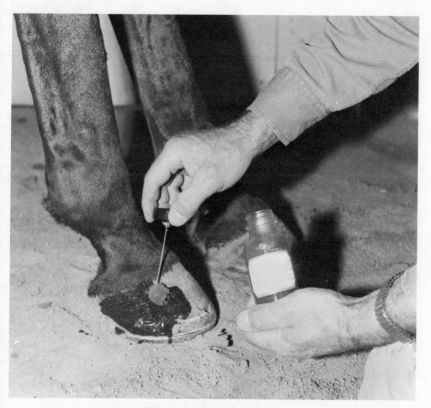

Fig. 49—Hoof Dressing

A good hoof dressing should be used after each shoeing, especially if you have to remove any of the outside wall. The dressing shown is a new dressing prepared by Dr. Keith Hoopes, DVM, and myself. It seals the hoof and softens it at the same time. We call it "Hoof Care" because that is what it does.

Shoeing the Balky Animal

One way to shoe a rough, hard-to-handle horse is as pictured in Figs. 50–55. Take a rope one-half inch or larger in diameter and about 10 feet long, and tie one end around the horse's neck so that it fits down around the shoulder. Run the other end down to the hind leg and through the rings of the leg strap. (*Fig. 50.*) Let the strap fall down around the pastern (*Fig. 51*) and then run the end of the rope back up to the loop around the neck (*Fig. 52*).

At this time be very careful because the horse may bolt as his foot is being pulled off the ground. Pull the foot about 18 inches off the ground and tie the rope securely (*Fig. 52*). Make the tie so that you can untie it fast if the horse throws himself (*Fig. 52*).

Let him stand for a few minutes so that he can get his balance and get over the shock of being handled roughly. After he has settled down, gently pull the leg out to the side and place the hoof on your leg (*Fig. 53*). He will be able to jerk his foot, but he will not be able to kick. You will find

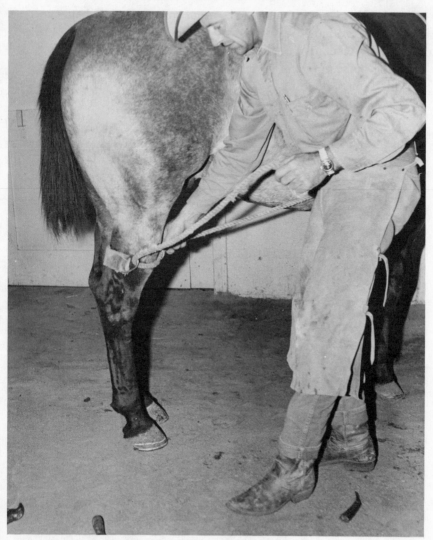

Fig. 50—Tying up the Hind Leg

If your horse is fussy with his hind feet, as many are, it may be necessary to tie up his legs. Start up here and then let the strap slide down as shown in Fig. 51.

that this is a hard way to shoe, but sometimes it is better to do it the hard way than to do it the unsafe way.

If you cannot do the job this way, you may have to throw the horse. He can be thrown easily if you put a hitch like this on both hind legs. However, instead of tying them, extend them back to the rear of the horse, with a man on

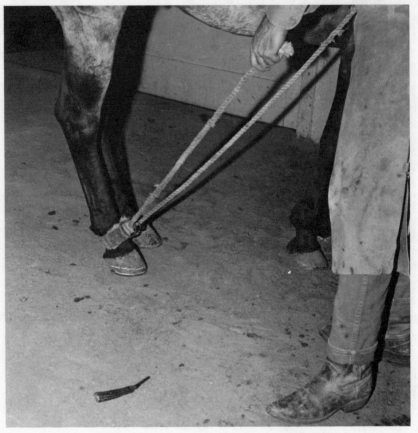

Fig. 51—Tying Up the Hind Leg (Contd.)
This shows the strap after it has been dropped to the pastern.

each rope and one on the halter rope, all pulling at the same time. When he is on the ground, be sure to tie all of his legs securely before you attempt to work on his feet. Remember that you cannot be too careful when you are handling the rough ones.

Another way to handle the rough one is to tie a foot up to his tail (*Fig. 55*). Use a soft cotton or nylon rope, about one-half inch in diameter. Form a bight in the tail; that is,

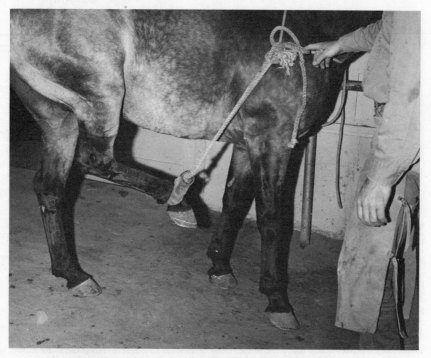

Fig. 52—Tying Up the Hind Leg (Contd.)

The leg has now been drawn up and the end of the rope tied in a slip knot that can be released by simply pulling on the end of the rope.

fold the tail back up, bring the rope end up through the bight, twist it over and under the bight, then bring it under itself (*Figs. 54, and 56 [a]*). If you don't have a leg strap (*Fig. 56 [b]*), run the rope around the pastern and pull the foot up to the tail and tie it in a knot that will be easy to undo in case of trouble.

Figure 56 shows an easy way to construct a leg strap.

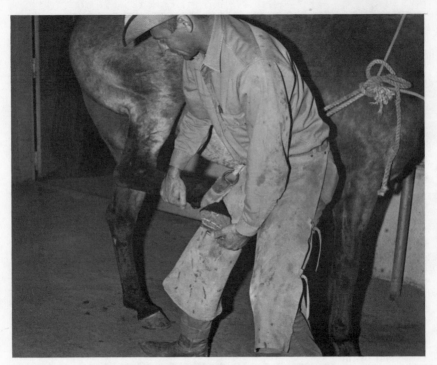

Fig. 53—Tying Up the Hind Leg (Contd.)

Pull the leg out away from the horse and lay it on your knee. He will still be able to struggle, but he will not be able to kick you.

Use a piece of latigo leather about 16 inches long. Double the ends back around 2-inch D rings and rivet with two copper rivets (Fig. 56 [c]). Put the washer and the burr on the under side. Then glue to the top side a piece of sheepskin. This will make a good soft padding, and you will find

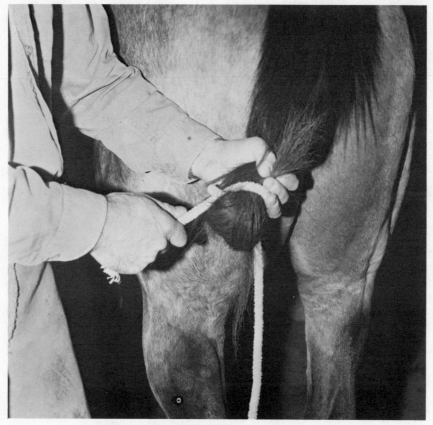

Fig. 54—The Tail Tie

Another way to tie the hind foot up is to tie a rope to the tail with a sheetbend. See Fig. 56.

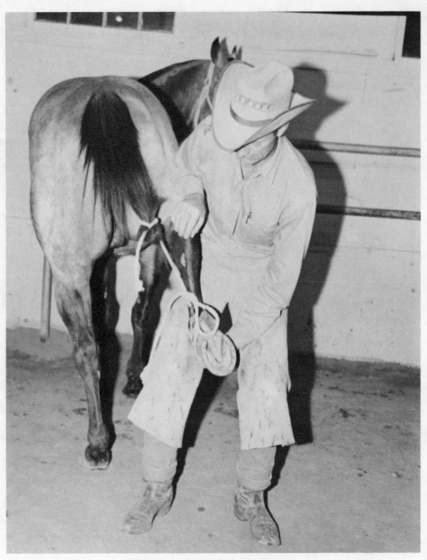

Fig. 55—The Tail Tie (Contd.)

The other end of the rope is tied to the leg strap, again using the slip knot. This is a good way to break a horse from lying on you while you are shoeing the rear feet.

(a) Sheetbend in Horse's Tail

(b) Leg Strap

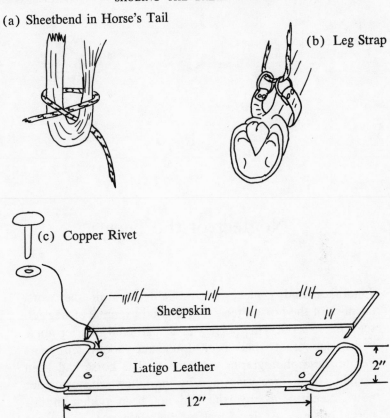

(c) Copper Rivet

Sheepskin

Latigo Leather

2″

12″

Fig. 56—The Leg Strap

that the horse will like it much better than the rope around the pastern. I have found that any time you can add a little comfort to the horse, you will get more than enough cooperation from the animal to offset the time it takes to add the comfort.

You will find that tying the foot up in this position will come in handy for horses that like to "lay" on you or that kick when they get tired.

Neglect of the Feet

Ignorance and neglect are probably two of the worst enemies of the horse's feet. For a good example of neglect, see Figs. 57–60. This horse was a registered quarter-horse which supposedly had been foundered about ten years before these photographs were taken. The horse had been bought about three years ago by the fellow who owns her now. Needless to say, she had not been ridden in this period of time. At first I was a little reluctant to trim these feet, but the owner assumed all responsibility if anything went wrong. I was reluctant to trim them because when a horse's feet are this bad from foundering, the coffin bone moves out into the toe of the foot. But as I cut away at the old horn, I realized that the hoof was long but in surprisingly good health. I believe that one reason for this was that the horse had been running in a soft wet pasture and the whole foot was soft. As you will note, the hoof is still a little long, but I didn't want to take too much off at once because the sudden change of the angle of the foot might

Figs. 57-60

These feet were badly neglected, as you can plainly see. But with proper care they were soon restored to near perfect health. Don't let this happen to your horse's feet. Trim them regularly.

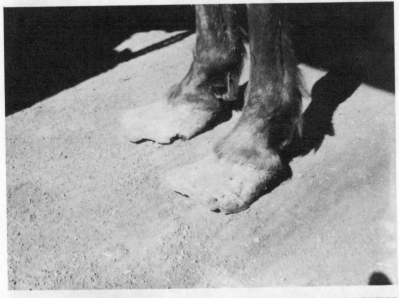

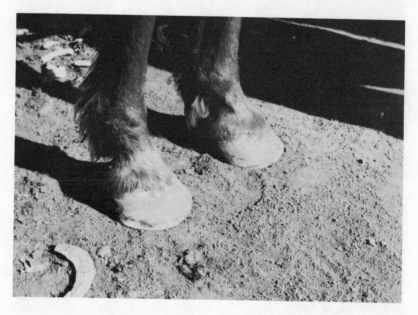

have made her lame. Also, when a hoof grows out long
like that, the blood vessels are out farther than they should
be and you could easily hit blood. Also the sensitive parts
of the foot are always near the surface. When you trim a
foot that is exceptionally long, it is better to take it down
a little at a time and not all at once. Wait about a week, then
repeat.

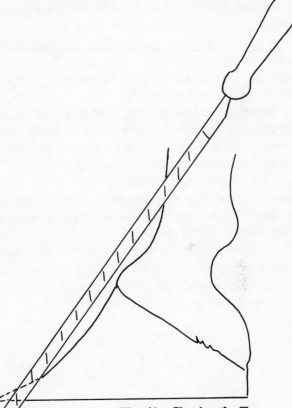

Fig. 61—Shaping the Toe

When removing excessive wall, make the cut as nearly the
same angle as the rest of the hoof, trying not to rasp the
upper part.

Normally it is not a good idea to cut the outer wall of the hoof as I have done on this horse, because when you do you remove the natural protection which is there. This protection is in the form of a varnishlike substance and is supplied only as the hoof is being developed around the coronary band. It comes from a gland called the perioplic ring and is called periople. Therefore, once it has been removed from the outer wall of the hoof, it is gone for good. If the wall has to be cut back like this, then the hoof should be treated with a good hoof dressing, such as "Hoof Care." The bad part about it is that when the hoof grows down it also grows out, usually in a dish shape. To do a good job of shoeing, the wall should be dressed down at the same angle as the rest of the foot (*see Fig. 61*).

Some of the best advice I can give you on the care of your horse's feet is to keep them trimmed and, if at all possible, have a damp place for them to stand in. This can be accomplished by merely flooding your watering trough and keeping a small puddle of water where the horse will have to stand in it to get a drink of water. He will absorb moisture up through the soles of his feet, keeping them from becoming hard and brittle.

BECAUSE THE HOOF GROWS ABOUT ONE THIRD INCH PER MONTH, TO KEEP YOUR HORSE'S FEET IN GOOD SHAPE THE SHOES SHOULD BE REMOVED, THE FEET TRIMMED AND RESHOD EVERY SIX TO EIGHT WEEKS.

Corrective Shoeing

I will not go into a lot of detail on corrective shoeing, but there are a few corrections of which you should be aware.

TURNING IN OR OUT

The most common fault you will come across is feet that either turn in or out. When they turn in, we call this base narrow or pigeon-toed. If they turn out, this is called base wide or splay footed. If the foot turns in, cut the hoof about 3/16 of an inch lower at the heel on the inside and blend with the other side at the toe (*Fig. 62*). This will force the weight of the horse to the inside and turn his foot out. If the foot turns out, cut the outside the same as described above. You will find that this will take care of all but the extreme cases. However, if the feet turn in or out because of poor conformation, all the corrective trimming and shoeing in the world will not change this problem. You will find that if you will keep the feet trimmed properly from

103

the time the horse is a colt, you will never have to worry about corrective measures.

If you are using the horse that is to be corrected, you should have shoes on him; but if he is not being used, you will get quicker and better results if you will leave the shoes off and rasp a little of the high side every two or three days.

OVERREACHING

Another correction you may be bothered with is over-reaching, sometimes called forging. This is when the horse overreaches with his hind feet and strikes his front. This, too, may be caused by poor conformation or excessive length of hoof. To correct this fault, leave the heels of the

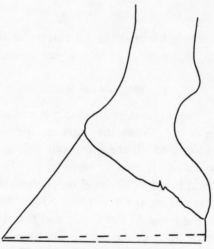

Fig. 62—Corrective Trimming

The dotted line shows the area to remove to correct base-wide or base-narrow front or rear feet. If a foot turns out cut as shown only on the outside blending in at the toe. If the foot turns in, cut the inside blending at the toe.

front feet a little long so he will be forced to stand up straighter and break over sooner. Cut the heels of the rear feet a little low; this will force him to set down on the hind feet and break over slower. This means that the front feet will now be out of the way before the rear feet come down. Remember, never make any change in a horse's feet too fast. Take a little off and then wait for a few days for him to become used to the change before you do the rest.

INTERFERING

Interfering is caused when one foot strikes the opposite leg as it passes by. This may be caused by faulty conformation or by improper shoeing. If conformation is at fault, there is little that can be done except to keep the foot properly shod. Set the shoe on the offending foot well under the hoof and trim the inside away slightly. Reset every three or four weeks. Also lower the outside heel and quarter of the foot on the injured leg. This will change the relative position of the fetlock joint, bringing away from the center plane and permitting the other foot to pass by more freely. Treat as a cut or wound. Cold water bandages will help to remove the swelling and soreness.

Bibliography

ADAMS, O. R. *Lameness in Horses.* Philadelphia: Lea and Febiger, 1962.

KAYS, D. J. *The Horse.* New York: A. S. Barnes and Company, 1953.

PEARSON, LEONARD, and others. *Diseases of the Horse.* Washington, D.C.: Government Printing Office, 1911.

The Western Horseman (compilation). *Horseshoeing and Hoof Care.* Denver: A. S. Hirshfeld Press, 1960.

Index